STORIES JESUS TOLD

Illustrated by Tony Morris

Brimax · Newmarket · England

As Jesus travelled from town to town, huge crowds would gather to listen to his stories. These stories are called parables, and they helped the people understand how God wanted them to lead their lives.

One story Jesus told was about a rich man who had two sons. The elder son was always busy and hard-working, but the younger son was very lazy.

One day the younger son said to his father, "Please will you give me my share of the money you intend to leave me when you die." The man did this and the younger son left home.

Instead of spending his money wisely, he wasted all he had. He bought himself expensive clothes and gifts, but never bothered to look for work. Soon all his money had gone.

Then a terrible famine spread throughout the country. The son was very hungry because he had no money for food. He went to many places looking for work. A farmer gave him the job of looking after his pigs. He was so hungry that he even wanted to eat the food that was given to the pigs.

Then one day the son decided to
return home to his father. "I will tell
him I am sorry, even though I no
longer deserve to be called his son,"
he said.

So the son returned home. When his father saw him he was filled with joy. He ran to his son and hugged him. "Father, please forgive me," said the young man. "I have sinned against you and against God."
But the man was so pleased to have his son back again, he ordered a feast to be prepared.

When the elder son saw that his brother had returned, he was angry. "Why are you preparing a feast?" he asked his father. "My brother wasted all his money." The man saw how upset his son was. "I thought I had lost my son forever," he replied. "But now he is found again." Jesus wanted to show the people that God loves everyone, and forgives those who can say they are sorry.

Another story was about the Good Samaritan.
One day, a man travelling from Jerusalem to Jericho was attacked by robbers. His money and donkey were stolen. He was beaten and left for dead.

A little while later, a priest passed by on his way to the Temple. He saw the injured man lying in the road but instead of stopping to help him, he carried on his way.

Soon another man passed by. He was a Levite — someone who helped at services in the Temple. He too saw the injured man lying in the road, but carried on his way without even stopping.

A little while after, a man from
Samaria came along the road. When
he saw the injured man he felt sorry
for him and washed his cuts with oil
and wine. Then he helped the man
onto his own donkey and took him to
an inn at the nearest village.

"Here is some money," he told the inn-keeper. "Look after this man. I will come back this way and give you more money if you need it."
Then Jesus asked the crowd, "Which of these men was the true friend?"
"The Samaritan," said the people.
"Then you should be the same," said Jesus. "Always help those who cannot help themselves."

Another story Jesus told was about a
servant who owed his master a great
deal of money.
"Your wife, children and all the land
you own must be sold to pay me,"
said the master.

The servant was terrified.
"Please give me some time," he begged. "I will pay back all that I owe you."
The master felt sorry for the man and forgave him the debt.

A short while later, the same man met a fellow servant who owed him a small amount of money.
"You must pay me what you owe," he said.
"Please give me some time," said the second servant. But the first servant had the man thrown into prison.

The servant's friends were very upset and went to the master to tell him what had happened.
The master was furious and called the servant to him.
"You have been cruel and unkind. I forgave you a debt, can you not forgive a debt, too?"

The servant was thrown into prison. Jesus told his listeners that they too had to learn to forgive one another.

All these appear in the pages of the story.
Can you find them?

rich man

inn-keeper

donkey

servant